Contents

Seek and Find

Can you find these objects in your book?

page 27

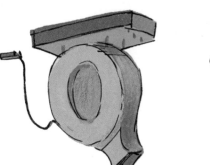

page 11

page 5

page 19

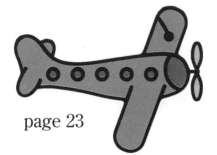

page 23

Cover illustration by Larry DiFiori

Solving Hidden Pictures puzzles develops figure-ground perception and improves the ability to establish object constancy and size relationships. Educators have shown that working on these puzzles can enhance a child's attention to detail, reinforce good work habits, increase word knowledge, and aid in developing self-confidence.

dragonfly

duck

doll

doughnut

drinking glass

dustpan

dog bone

drum

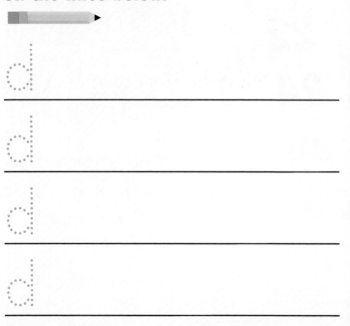

dolphin

dish

Illustrated by Valeri Gorbachev

Try to write some of your favorite words that begin with d on the lines below.

d _____

d _____

d _____

d _____

These 8 funny things are happening in the scene.
Can you find them all? Answers on page 30

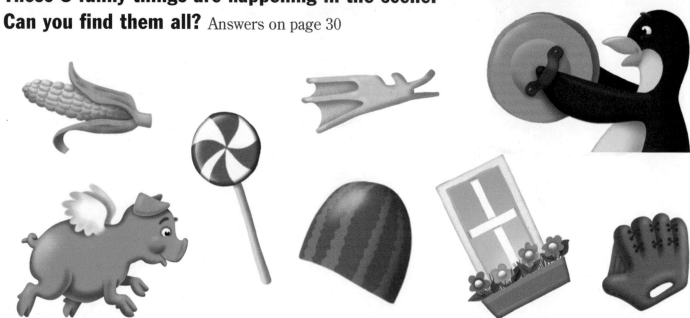

Imagine and Draw

What is the silliest thing someone might do on a stage? Draw a picture of it here.

| CRAYON |

Illustrated by Nathan Y. Jarvis

Olivia and Tyler are helping their father build a new doghouse for their favorite pet.

Can you find these hidden objects on the next page?

Answers on page 30

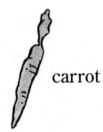

carrot

butterfly

bat

string

lollipop

balloon

cane

duck

Illustrated by Larry DiFiori

Can you guess the answer to each riddle? Use the Hidden Pictures™ words if you need help.

There is lots of air inside me.

Sometimes I pop too soon.

I come in many colors.

I am a round _____.

I am a mammal who has wings.

I fly around at night.

Do you know what they call me?

If you guessed _____, you're right!

To fly a kite or spin a top,

Use me—I'm just the thing.

I'm like some rope, but thinner.

I am a ball of _____.

Cherry, lemon, orange, lime—

My flavors never stop.

I am a candy on a stick.

That's right, a _____.

Can you find the Hidden Pictures on the lake? When you finish, you can color

DREAMBOAT

Place these stickers on the hidden objects as you find them.

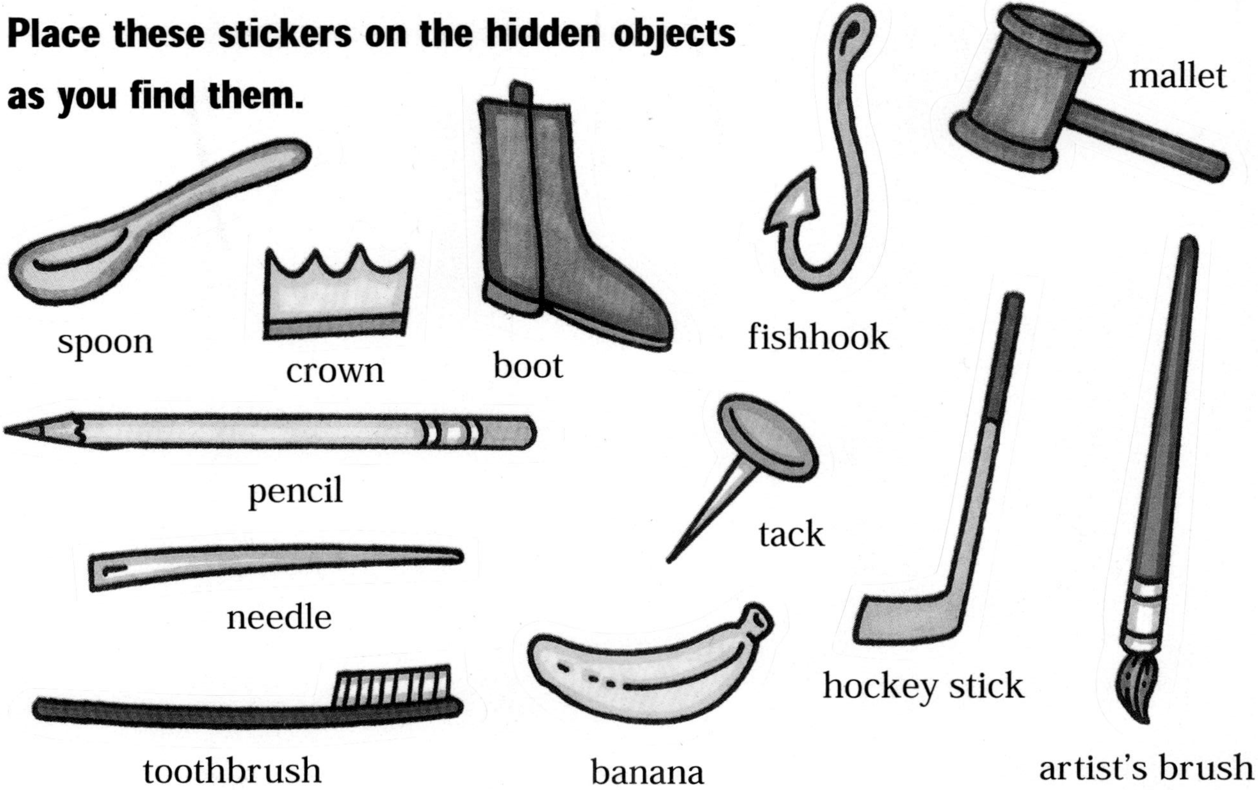

toothbrush

needle

pencil

spoon

crown

boot

banana

tack

fishhook

hockey stick

mallet

artist's brush

Boating

in the rest of the scene. | CRAYON | Answers on page 30   Illustrated by R. Michael Palan

FISHY

Wheel Search

Can you find 10 wheels on the next page? Answers on page 3

Color in a wheel in this box each time you find a wheel in the picture. CRAYON

Connect the dots from 1 to 25 to find something that is lots of fun.

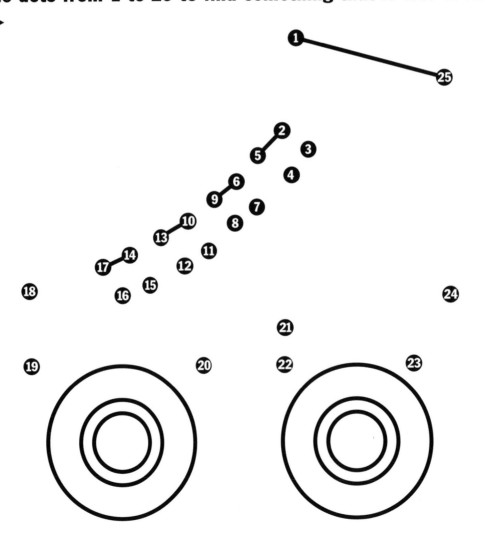

At the bake sale, you can buy cupcakes, cookies, cakes, and pies. Yum!

Can you find these Hidden Pictures™ on the next page? Answers on page 31

screwdriver

saw

hammer

teacup

canoe

candle

ice-cream cone

artist's brush

Use your crayons to finish this birthday cake. Don't forget to add the candles!

CRAYON

CREAMY FROSTING

**Hidden Pictures time to rhyme.
You can find them every time.**

Do you see a  baseball bat?
And over there, a party hat!

Spot a tasty wedge of cheese,
A tissue box in case you sneeze.

La-la-la, I hear a note,
And row, row, row a tiny boat.

Try to spy an open book,
A frying pan used by a cook.

Do you see a piece of cork?
How about a shiny fork?

**You first found one and then the rest.
Hip! Hip! Hooray! You are the best!**

Answers on page 31

Illustrated by Philomena O'Neill

THE CANDY SHOP

TIME OUT
WATCHES FOR MEN AND WOMEN

Can you find the Hidden Pictures below? When you finish, you can color

Place these stickers on the hidden objects as you find them.

trowel

envelope

slice of bread

bell

feather

baseball

flower

mug

pencil

toothbrush

spool of thread

mallet

Answers on page 31

in the rest of the picture. CRAYON   Illustrated by Rocky Fuller

Alyssa is buying a birthday present for her cat, Boots.

Can you find these animals in the picture on the next page?
Be sure to find the right number of each. Answers on page 31

1 dog **2** cats **3** rabbits **4** mice **5** birds **6** fish

Illustrated by Monica Wellington

Color in each shape that has a dot in it. When you finish, you will see an unusual pet.

║ CRAYON ║►

Tyler Turnipseed lived in a very noisy family. His father drove a truck that roared and rumbled. His mother was a carpenter and banged on nails with a **hammer**. His grandmother played the **banjo** and the piano. When she did, Tyler's dog, Boomer, dropped his **bone** and howled along. Every Fourth of July the whole family loved to set off loud fireworks. But not Tyler. Tyler was quiet as a **mouse**. In fact, the quieter it was, the better Tyler liked it.

Tyler looked at the calendar. It was almost December 31. Tyler had circled the date with a **pencil**. That was his birthday.

"What do you want for your birthday, Tyler?" asked his father. "How about a **horn** for your bicycle?"

Tyler smiled and shook his head.

"I know what you'd like," said his mother. "A **whistle**."

"No, thanks," said Tyler quietly.

"When I was your age, I really wanted a **drum**!" said his grandmother. "Is that what you want?"

"No," said Tyler.

"Well, what do you want for your birthday, Tyler?" everyone shouted.

Tyler smiled. He knew what he wanted, and it wasn't noisy at all. "I would like a sled," he said. Then he looked out the window at the bare ground and thought of the quietest thing he knew. "And lots of snow."

A Hidden Pictures™ Story by Marileta Robinson

Can you find the hidden objects from the story in this scene? Answers on page 32

car

sock

button

football

cap

mug

Each object is hidden two times—once in each scene. We found and circled the mugs. Can you find the others? Answers on page 32

hammer

flowerpot

glove

skate

kite

toothbrush

Can you find the Hidden Pictures below? When you finish, you can color

Place these stickers on the hidden objects as you find them.

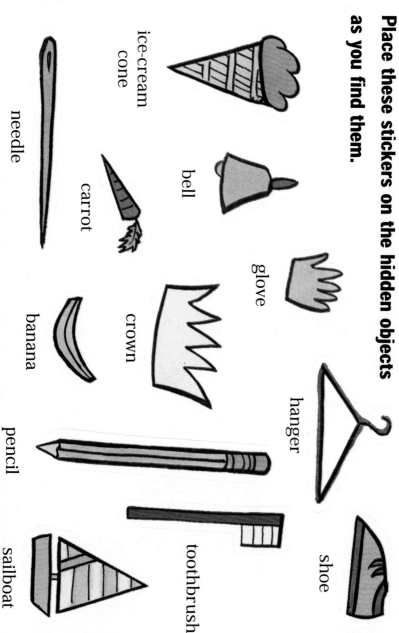

needle

ice-cream cone

carrot

bell

glove

banana

crown

hanger

pencil

toothbrush

shoe

sailboat

in the rest of the picture. CRAYON ➡ Answers on page 32   Illustrated by Timothy Davis

Leo the artist has painted a picture of himself.

Can you find these shapes in the picture on the next page? Answers on page 32

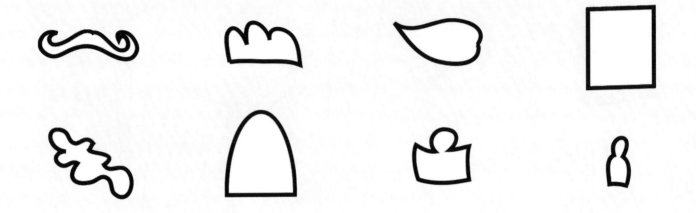

**When you draw
a picture of
yourself,
it is called
a self-portrait.**

**Draw your
self-portrait
here.**

║ CRAYON ║

**Be sure to write
your name
on your drawing
when you
are finished.**

Hidden Pictures™

Ashley is teaching her little brother, Brandon, to play checkers.

There are 12 objects hidden in this picture. How many can you find?

Answers on page 32

handbell

zipper

comb

The names of the 12 objects are hidden below. Some are across. Others are up and down. Find and circle each word.

duck

pie

x	p	i	e	q	j	y	x
h	a	n	d	b	e	l	l
o	c	y	d	u	c	k	o
c	o	s	h	a	r	k	c
t	m	f	o	r	k	j	k
o	b	q	j	y	v	v	x
p	b	u	t	t	o	n	r
u	q	v	y	j	j	y	i
s	t	a	r	x	v	q	n
x	z	i	p	p	e	r	g

fork

star

button

lock

ring

shark

octopus

Answers

Cover

Hidden Pictures™ ABC pages 2–3

Silly Stage page 5

A House for Juno pages 6–7

There is lots of air inside me.
Sometimes I pop too soon.
I come in many colors.
I am a round **balloon**.

I am a mammal who has wings.
I fly around at night.
Do you know what they call me?
If you guessed **bat**, you're right!

To fly a kite or spin a top,
Use me—I'm just the thing.
I'm like some rope, but thinner.
I am a ball of **string**.

Cherry, lemon, orange, lime—
My flavors never stop.
I am a candy on a stick.
That's right, a **lollipop**.

Boating pages 8–9

Answers

Wheel Search pages 10–11

It's a roller skate!

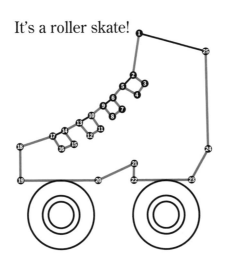

Cookies and Cake page 13

Hidden Pictures™ Rhymes pages 14–15

Pet Shop pages 18–19

It's a lizard!

Car Race pages 16–17

Answers

**Happy Birthday,
Tyler Turnipseed page 21**

Double Hidden Pictures™ pages 22–23

Hoedown pages 24–25

Find the Shapes page 27

Hidden Pictures Hidden Words pages 28–29